Tap, Tap!

By Janice Pimm
Illustrations by Jon Stuart

OXFORD

UNIVERSITY PRESS

In this story ...

💬 **TALK**

- Introduce children to the characters in this story: Max, Ant and Max's mum.
- Point to the words that represent the characters' names and say each of the names together. Children will meet these words in the story.

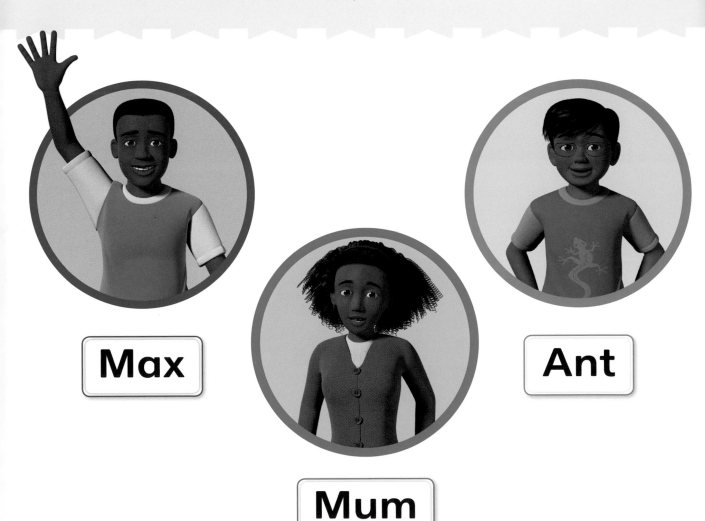

Max

Mum

Ant

Max and Ant have special watches. When they push the buttons on their watches they can shrink to micro-size, like this ...

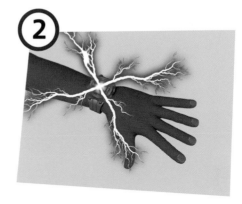

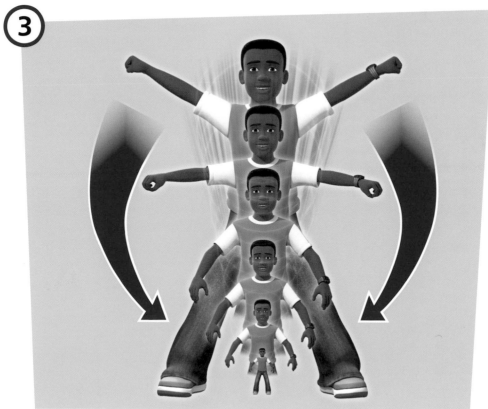

They become tiny and can have amazing adventures!

It was a sunny day at the seaside. Max's mum was helping Max and Ant build a sandcastle.

"Tap it with your spade," said Mum. "Pat it with your hands."

💬 **TALK**

- What are Max and Ant building? Ask children to describe it.

👥 **ACTIVITY**

- Say the word *sandcastle* and ask children to repeat it. What sound does the word *sandcastle* begin with? Remember to use the *sound* of the letter, not the letter name.
- Ask children to spot other objects in the picture that begin with the /s/ sound (e.g. seaweed, spade).

★ **Tip**

See the inside back cover for more guidance on sounds.

Max taps. Ant pats.

When the sandcastle was finished, Mum sat down for a rest. She closed her eyes and went to sleep.

"Let's shrink to play in our sandcastle," said Ant. "If we are small, it will feel like a real castle!"

Max and Ant pushed the buttons on their watches to shrink to micro-size. Wow! Suddenly, the sandcastle was huge!

Ant climbed right to the top and sat on the wall.

Max climbed the steps too fast. He tripped and landed with a bump!

Ant sat. Max sat.

tap

tap

📖 READ

Suddenly, the children heard a tapping noise.

"What is that?" cried Max.

"It's coming this way," said Ant.

💬 TALK

- Ask children to say what they think might be happening. What could be making the tapping noise? What clues are there in the picture?
- How might Max and Ant be feeling?

👥 ACTIVITY

- Point to the word *tap* on the page and ask children to sound-talk it (i.e. tap becomes t-a-p). Ask children to tap a finger on a table as they say each sound.
- Then ask children to blend the sounds together and say the word (i.e. t-a-p becomes tap).

tap

tap

📖 READ

Just then a giant crab appeared. It tapped at the sandcastle with its giant claws. The walls began to crumble.

"Yikes!" cried Max.

"Run!" yelled Ant.

💬 TALK

- Tell children some crab facts!
  - Crabs live by the sea.
  - Crabs have hard bodies and a pair of sharp claws.
  - Crabs have ten legs and walk sideways!
  - Can you make your hands pinch like crab claws?

👥 ACTIVITY

- Say the word *run* and ask children to sound-talk it (i.e. run becomes r-u-n). Ask children to make running actions with their arms as they say each sound.
- Then ask children to blend the sounds together and say the word (i.e. r-u-n becomes run).

READ

Max and Ant escaped. They pushed the buttons on their watches and grew back to normal size.

"We're safe now," said Max. "But the crab has broken our sandcastle."

"We can pat it back together," said Ant.

💬 TALK

- How might Max and Ant be feeling now?
- Max's mum is sleeping. What noise might she make while she sleeps? Have fun making snoring noises!

👥 ACTIVITY

- **Have some fun!** Ask children to make their own sandcastle in a sandpit or sand tray!

Max taps. Ant pats.

12